SAME OLD STORY!

The family was a bit taken aback when my uncle announced he was going to marry a widow who's twenty years older than him.

Mum was fascinated by the news. She asked Dad all about the woman and discovered she and Uncle Ron had met at a local night school.

"What subject?" Mum inquired.

Her face was a picture when he answered calmly:

"I'm not certain, but I think it was 'collecting antiques'!"

Sandy, Newcastle.

OH BOY!

One of my friends is a real bore. She's boy mad.

After a couple of us gave her a serious talking-to she took up another hobby — astronomy.

"That's much better isn't it?" I confided in a friend. "I'm so glad she spends her time peering at the stars."

"The *moon*, you mean," my witty friend joked, "she's looking to see if there's really a man in it!"

I had to laugh!

Kathy, Liverpool.

BREATH-TAKING

I get colds all Winter long and am always looking for miracle cures for them. My friend's brother is a medical student and he told me about how one of his lecturers advised them all to eat a raw onion every morning in Winter.

"Does that kill the germs?" I asked eagerly.

"I shouldn't think so," he replied, "but if that bloke's breath is anything to go by . . . it probably stops anyone getting close enough to pass them on!"

Amber, Shrewsbury.

DOG-GONE IT!

I was very impressed when a friend said her family had got a dog. When I asked the breed she said it was a 'bitza'.

As I always make out that I know a lot about dogs I didn't like to let on that I'd never heard of it, and decided to look it up in my book as soon as I got home. No good . . . I couldn't find the breed listed anywhere.

"Are you sure your new dog's called a bitza?" I asked her the very next day.

"No, it's not *called* that, it *is* that . . . bitza this and bitsa that!" How was I to know that that's another name for a mongrel?!

Louise, Hapton.

CHEAP FRILLS?

My brother's friend was bemoaning the fact that he could never be a pop star 'cos he didn't have a sister.

"Why's that important?" I asked, bewildered.

"Well, I have to have clothes to practise in," he answered.

Hannah, Staffs.

REVENGE IS SWEET

I had a real laugh when I went swimming at our local baths recently with my best friend.

It seems they're getting a bit strict, 'cos there was a huge notice pinned up on the wall saying: 'We don't swim in your loos so please don't pee in our pool.'

Quite right too — I reckon some people have got disgusting habits!

Kim, Dalston.

£3.25

if I WERE you...

Do you know all about the girl you call your friend? You're sure? Then try our quiz! Work through all the questions, all the time thinking hard about your friend's likes and dislikes. When you've written down all your answers get her to go through them to see how many you got right.

If she's shocked that you seem to know so little about her, why not turn the tables, and get her to answer the questions as she expects you to!

1. Which of these programmes would she prefer to watch:
a) Top of the Pops?
b) Brookside?
c) A prog about her favourite sport or hobby?

2. Has she ever had a ride on a horse?
Yes/No.

3. If she were choosing a pet would she prefer:
a) A cat?
b) A dog?
c) A rabbit?
(If she can't stand animals, which of the above does she dislike the least?!)

4. Which of these take-away meals would be her usual favourite:
a) A hamburger?
b) A hot dog?
c) Fish and chips?

5. Is her attitude to homework usually:
a) To get it done at the earliest opportunity, so she can make use of her free time?
b) To leave it till the night before (or even the hour before) it has to be handed in?
c) Not to do it at all, if she can get away with it, or find someone to copy from?

6. If she got an unexpected amount of cash would she be likely to:
a) Buy clothes?
b) Buy records?
c) Save it?

7. Which of the following fellas does she prefer:
a) Simon Le Bon?
b) George from Wham!?
c) Nik Kershaw?

8. If she were going to a friend's fancy dress party would she prefer to go as:
a) Anything that meant she could still look pretty?
b) Anything that meant she didn't have to go to a lot of trouble?
c) Anything where she could wear a mask and she wouldn't be recognised?

9. If her family were about to increase, would she prefer to have:
a) A brother?
b) A sister?
c) One of each?

10. If she could visit one of these exotic places it'd be:
a) Japan?
b) Malaysia?
c) South America?

11. Which of the following presents would she be most disappointed to receive:
a) A pen and pencil set?
b) A book of poetry?
c) Writing paper?

12. Would she prefer to get a gift of:
a) A fiver immediately?
b) Fifty pounds next Xmas?
c) A thousand pounds at the age of 18?

13. When she has a bath, does she run . . .
a) The hot water first, then top up with cold?
b) The cold water first, then tops up with hot?
c) The hot and cold water at the same time?
(Of course you've really no way of knowing. That's why you've got to work it out from what you know about her!)

14. If she's cutting a sandwich, does she cut it:
a) Diagonally so two triangular sandwiches are left?
b) Straight across — into two sandwiches?
c) She'd never cut it in half, no matter what size it was?

15. If a fortune teller offered to forecast her future would she:
a) Have it done happily if she had the money?
b) Have it done only if it didn't involve money or inconvenience?
c) Rather not?

16. It's sports time at school. Does she:
a) Change and rush out there straight away as keen as mustard?
b) Limply trail out onto the sports field?
c) Make some sort of excuse to your teacher that she can't play?

17. Mum has asked you to babysit. You'd planned to go out with your best friend that same night. Would she:
a) Make a date for the following night?
b) Have a good long chat over the phone instead?
c) Come straight round and help you babysit?

18. Does she ever cheat in school tests?
Yes/No.

COMPUTER GAMES

9

MUM'S RIGHT, I SHOULDN'T HAVE MADE HER AND DAD WASTE ALL THAT MONEY ON ME. . .

But a few minutes later. . .

LORRAINE! LORRAINE, WAIT!

TONY!

I'VE JUST BEEN ROUND TO YOUR HOUSE. YOUR MUM TOLD ME YOU'D BE COMING THIS WAY. HEY, WHY DIDN'T YOU TELL ME YOUR NAME WAS REALLY LORRAINE?

BUT I. . .OH, NEVER MIND. WHAT DID YOU WANT, TONY?

WELL, I KNOW IT SOUNDS STUPID, BUT I CAME OVER TO ASK IF YOU'D LIKE TO COME OVER AND LOOK AT MY COMPUTER?

OH, TONY, I'D LOVE TO!

I KEPT MEANING TO ASK YOU ALL WEEK, BUT I DIDN'T KNOW WHAT TO SAY.

I UNDERSTAND, TONY.

I WISH HE'D MENTIONED IT THIS MORNING, THOUGH, THEN I WOULD'VE HAD TIME TO WASH MY HAIR!

YOU GO UP, I'LL MAKE US SOME COFFEE. MY ROOM'S THE FIRST ON THE LEFT.

THANKS.

MEET... THE SÜPERFANS!

WHAT THE FANS SAY...

"I think it's stupid, the way some girls go mad over pop stars. I mean, I really like George Michael, but there's no way I'd ever stand at a freezing cold airport for three days just to catch a glimpse of him! I'd rather stay at home and look at his picture instead!"

Louise, Maidstone.

"My friend once waited four hours to see Duran Duran come out of 'Saturday Superstore'. Then when they did come out, all the other girls pushed forward and she didn't even get to see their car! But the stupid thing was, she still said it was worth it!"

Clare, Croydon.

"I think I'm a Superfan. I get £2 pocket money a week and I spend all of it on Culture Club. I buy all their records — 7 and 12 inch versions — and I've covered all my walls, my books and my desk at school with their pictures. Also I travelled all the way down to Wembley to see them in concert. My mum and dad think I'm a bit mad, but I don't mind paying all that money or travelling miles to see Culture Club. I think anyone who isn't prepared to do the same, can't be a real fan."

Lisa, Liverpool.

They're the faces you see at the airport every time a pop star arrives, the nameless girls who'd stand freezing in the cold for three days, tie themselves to cars and scream themselves rigid just to get a good look at their idol. Could you be one of them? Read on and find out if you're a Superfan!

1. You're all set to go on the holiday of a lifetime — when you hear your idol's playing in your town on the day you're due to leave! Do you:
a) Forget your disappointment and enjoy your holiday — he's bound to play in your town again one day?
b) Go on holiday, but beg your mate to get you a tour brochure and t-shirt?
c) Pretend you've got the dreaded Beri Beri disease so you don't have to go on holiday?

2. You read in the papers that your favourite pop star has just got engaged. And you thought he'd wait for you! Do you:
a) Tear down all your pictures of him and vow never to speak his name again. He's really let you down — the swine!?
b) Shed a few tears but feel happy that he's found the right girl for him (even if it wasn't you!)?
c) Start liking someone else instead?

3. How many pictures have you got of your favourite pop star?
a) 50-100?
b) You lose count after 500?
c) What pictures?

4. Someone you know says something extremely nasty about your idol. Do you:
a) Agree — you don't want to fall out with her?
b) Threaten to punch her if she doesn't take back all her nasty remarks straight away?
c) Ignore her. She's only trying to wind you up and besides, how can you argue with someone who's got no taste!?

5. Your favourite pop star's making a guest appearance at your local record shop. Do you:
a) Turn up three days early and start queuing. Who cares if it's mid-winter and three degrees below freezing?
b) Forget until the last minute then turn up just in time to see his car speeding away?
c) Bribe someone at the shop to save you a personally signed copy of his latest record?

6. Somehow you manage to find out your favourite pop star's home address. Do you:
a) Make a note to keep it a secret. He deserves his privacy?
b) Sell it to all your mates for a fiver a time?
c) Spend all your time hanging about outside, scrawling 'I love you' lovingly into the paintwork of his Rolls Royce?

7. On your favourite pop star's birthday, do you send him:
a) A massive card and a huge cuddly toy that takes the postman three days to get through his letterbox. He won't forget you in

a hurry. (And neither will the postman!)?
b) A card that you made yourself?
c) Nothing. You forgot — again!?

8. Is your first thought on waking up in the morning:
a) "I wonder what *he's* doing right now?"?
b) "I wonder if this will be the day I finally get to meet him?"?
c) Oh no, it's morning — time for school again!"?

SCORE

	a	b	c
1	0	5	10
2	10	5	0
3	5	10	0
4	0	10	5
5	10	0	5
6	5	0	10
7	10	5	0
8	5	10	0

HOW DID YOU DO?

0—25. Call yourself a fan? You don't exactly put yourself out for your favourite star, do you? You forget his birthday, you don't have any pictures of him . . . we get the feeling you only like him because everyone else does!

30—55. You're a Superfan all right! Okay, so you might not have all your walls plastered with his pictures, and you may not queue for three weeks just to catch a glimpse of him, but you love his music and more important, you respect his privacy. You're just the kind of fan the stars love to have!

60—80. You might think you're a superfan, but there's more to liking a pop star than collecting his pictures and fainting whenever you hear his name mentioned! You make the mistake of thinking that pop stars are public property, with no lives of their own. In which case you should think again. Not every pop star likes having all his clothes ripped off every time he sets foot out of the door, you know!

WHAT THE STARS SAY...

"Our fans are great but sometimes they can be a bit frightening — especially when they gang up on you!"
Spandau Ballet.

"Most of my fans are really friendly when you get them on their own. It's just when they're all together they scare me."
Howard Jones.

"When we were in Japan a couple of years ago the hotel was completely surrounded by screaming fans. We were trapped. It was absolutely terrifying!"
Duran Duran.

"I find generally fans are nice people. They just don't seem to realise that you're a human being too, and you can get hurt just like anyone else when fifty screaming girls descend on you!
"I've had some pretty close shaves but have somehow survived. I love my fans — but please take it easy!"
Nik Kershaw.

LIMAHL:

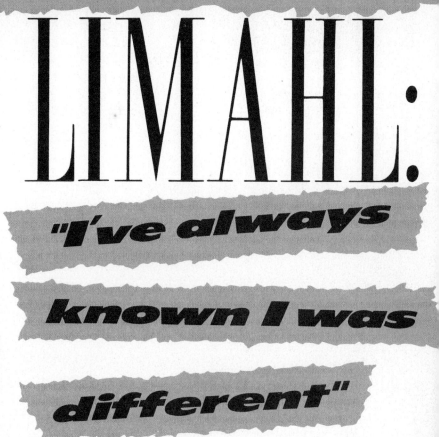

"I've always known I was different"

When Christopher Hamill — better known as Limahl — was just four years-old, his mother went along to see a fortune teller.

"You have a young son," she was told, "and one day he's going to be very famous, he's going to be a star!"

No wonder Limahl says he knew exactly what he wanted to do from a very early age!

"Even when I was that young, I did have a feeling of being slightly *different*," he remembers. "It wasn't that I thought I was better than my family or friends, I just knew that settling down to a

job in a factory and marriage at 20 wasn't for me.

"I was born and brought up in Wigan, and though I had a happy childhood, that sense of being different always spurred me on. I liked to dress up in outrageous clothes and dance literally all night at the famous Northern Soul discos.

"If you were quite good-looking and fashionable in Wigan, you had to leave, really. There was nothing there to fulfil my kind of ambition."

That ambition was always to be a performer. Limahl remembers singing on buses and in shops — anywhere he could get an audience — when he was small, and he always had a flair for style and

make-up. Eventually, he left home at 16 and began his career proper.

"I actually started out in hairdressing," he says. "I liked it, too. It was something creative, you see, and that suited me fine."

To this day, Limahl makes good use of his early training.

"I'm probably a real pain for my hairdressser," he grins. "I'm always going, 'not too much off the

top, mind the sides . . .' ."

After hairdressing, he was lured by the bright lights of the theatre and appeared in a few pantos and local theatre productions before coming to London.

"I always loved acting *and* singing" he says. "In theatre, I'd been doing acting with a bit of singing. I decided that I really wanted to do singing with a bit of acting thrown in."

In London he joined forces with a four-piece band who'd been together for some time. They called themselves Kajagoogoo, and went on to have a hugely successful year as pop stars.

But things went wrong and the rest of the band decided they no longer wanted to work with Limahl.

He was sacked.

"That hurt me badly," he says. "I was obviously very upset and bitter. But looking back, I realise that they did me the biggest favour of my life!"

It's easy to see why he feels that way. Kajagoogoo went through a period of very little success until they became virtual has-beens. Limahl, on the other hand, had a Top Twenty Hit with his first solo single, *Only for Love* . . . then nothing. Although he continued to be hugely popular in Europe and Australia it was almost a year until his next British chart success, the haunting *Never Ending Story*.

"I was scared, I have to admit it," he says, "but that hit restored all my confidence!"

Just like that fortune teller told his mum, Limahl is destined to be a very big star indeed!

Captain Sensible

COLOUR CRAZY!

Ever wondered why you make a bee-line for certain colours when you're out shopping for clothes? What you wear colour wise is also quite a character guide! Read on . . .

YELLOW PERIL

Yellow is a sunshine colour and if you like this colour it shows you're full of the joys of Spring! It's not a colour that looks good on everyone though, so be careful wearing it. Ask your mates for their opinion!

IN THE RIGHT LIGHT...

Lovers of light colours like whites, beiges and creams show a person who's crisp and clean! You're also a girl who pays quite a bit of attention to how you look. A stunning white outfit, 'specially in Summer, can really stand out! These colours look good on most people, just so long as they're kept extra clean.

GREEN FOR GO

Green shows you've got a peaceful nature — after all, it's one of the most calming colours in the colour spectrum. Wearing green shows you're very much a Summer person and that you like the sun and warmth. Again, it's not a colour that suits everyone. So do be careful when you're buying it.

IN THE PINK!

Pinkies are generally very feminine and fluffy people. It's an appealing and soft colour that comes in many shades. If you wear masses of pink you'll have a warm personality. If you're a lover of vivid pink, it shows that you also like standing out in a crowd. Good on any hair colour — except red-heads, of course!

BLUE FOR YOU...

Blue is a sophisticated colour. People that like this colour are very together and organised! They always look well turned out. Blue looks good on most people so wear it when you want to look super smart and want to impress someone special in your life.

SEEING RED...

If you like wearing bright red it's a sure sign that you like standing out in a crowd! Definitely not a colour for the shy and timid. Girls that wear red have colourful personalities to match. It looks 'specially good on blondes, although girls with very black hair suit it too!

BLACK MOODS

Black and browns — you can get moody and fed-up at times. Be careful wearing these colours because they can look just plain dowdy. Try them out and see — you might be lucky enough to look terrific in either! But steer clear if you're not sure.

PURPLE POWER

If you like this colour it shows you've got a strong and dominating character! Lilac is much more appealing and very fashionable. Be careful purple doesn't 'drain' your skin tones if you wear this colour close to your face. You could end up looking awful!

Tracey Ullman

Howard Jones

Paul Young

SECRET of the SKULLS

In the spring of the year 1666 London suffered the worst storms in living memory. The Thameside church of St. Leofric's-by-the-Wall offered better shelter to its poor parishioners than their wooden hovels.

They were glad of the bread and soup given out by Parson Sylvester and his only daughter, Prudence.

FATHER, WHAT WAS THAT TERRIBLE CRASH? IT-IT FELT LIKE LIGHTNING STRIKING THE CHURCH.

HUSH, CHILD. WE ARE IN GOD'S HOUSE — NO HARM CAN COME TO US. NOW RUN TO THE HOUSE AND SEE IF MRS. MARCH HAS ANY MORE SOUP READY.

OH, MISS PRUDENCE — I CAME TO SEE IF YOU WERE ALL SAFE. A THUNDERBOLT HIT THE CHURCH.

WE ARE UNHARMED, MRS. MARCH, BUT WHERE IS QUIST?

Quist the gravedigger was safe enough, but horrified at the damage the lightning had done to the church.

THE WALL BENEATH THE VESTRY'S COLLAPSED. BEST SEE WHAT I CAN DO.

BEHIND THIS WALL — 'TIS SOME KIND OF CRYPT AND LORDA MERCY! IT CAN'T BE TRUE! WHAT A FOUL SIGHT!

ARE YOU ALL RIGHT, MR. QUIST?

BACK, BACK! YOU MUST NOT SEE. WHERE IS THE PARSON?

WELL, WHAT IS IT, MAN? SPEAK UP!

'TIS TOO HORRIBLE FOR WORDS. LET ME TAKE YOU, MASTER!

VERY WELL. MRS. MARCH, HELP FEED MY FLOCK. PRUE, FETCH A LANTERN AND COME WITH ME.

THERE IS NOTHING TO FEAR IN GOD'S HOUSE, MR. QUIST.

WHY, IT'S AN ANCIENT CRYPT NO ONE HAS KNOWN OF BEFORE! THAT'S ALL, QUIST!

THEN WHY ARE THERE ONLY SKULLS HERE — AND NOTHING ELSE? THE PLACE IS EVIL — CAN'T YOU FEEL IT?

I SHALL HAVE THE SKULLS REMOVED TO A PROPER BURIAL PLACE AND BLESSED.

IF YOU'VE ANY SENSE YOU WON'T TOUCH 'EM. SEAL THE PLACE UP AGAIN AND FORGET 'EM. BRICK THE EVIL IN — I SAY.

IS EVERYTHING ALL RIGHT? THE CHURCH WON'T COLLAPSE?

NO DANGER AT ALL, MY DEAR MRS. MARCH.

27

31

32

Continued on page 81

33

The Legend of
FENLEY HILLS

When Penny and Val told Linda about the legend of Fenley Hills, they didn't know what they'd started. . .

HELLO, VAL, I KNEW IT'D BE YOU. HAVE YOU BROUGHT THOSE MAGAZINES?

ER. . .AND SOMETHING ELSE BESIDES.

HI THERE, PEN, YOU DON'T MIND IF I COME TOO? NO, I THOUGHT YOU WOULDN'T.

HELLO LINDA.

35

IF YOU START SPLASHING I'M GETTING STRAIGHT OUT.

AND SWIMMING POOL

CISSY – CAN'T YOU STAND A BIT OF WATER? YOU OUGHT TO LEARN TO SWIM PROPERLY LIKE VAL AND ME.

Nothing Val or Penny said could get rid of Linda. She stuck to them like superglue.

I WENT UP THE HILLS THIS MORNING WALKING RUSTY, THEY LOOKED REALLY LOVELY.

THEY'RE NOTHING SPECIAL.

HAVE YOU HEARD THE LEGEND ABOUT THE HILLS?

WHAT LEGEND?

OUT OF THE CAVE COMES AN OLD MAN, THE GHOST OF A HERMIT THAT ONCE LIVED THERE.

THE ONE ABOUT THE HERMIT'S CAVE. WHEN IT'S MISTY AND THE HILLS ARE COVERED IN FOG, THERE'S SUPPOSED TO BE A CAVE THAT OPENS IN THE HILLSIDE.

YOU MAKE IT SOUND LIKE JACKANORY.

SO YOU DON'T BELIEVE IT?

NO, IT'S A LOAD OF RUBBISH. IF THERE WERE SUCH A THING AS GHOSTS I'D HAVE SEEN ONE BY NOW.

IT WOULD HAVE TO BE YOU THAT SEES ONE FIRST.

OKAY THEN, THE NEXT TIME THE HILLS ARE COVERED IN MIST, WE'LL GO UP THERE, ALL THREE OF US AND LOOK FOR THIS CAVE – UNLESS, OF COURSE, YOU'RE SCARED?

I'M NOT SCARED.

As Penny turned she saw the strange old man coming towards her.

She stood there, rooted to the spot, as slowly the figure advanced.

YOU **REALLY** FRIGHTENED ME THEN. EVEN THOUGH I KNEW IT WAS YOU I WAS STILL SCARED.

It had all been a trick. The hermit was Val dressed in a mask and cape.

DID IT LOOK GOOD?

YOU'RE KIDDING, LINDA WAS PETRIFIED! SHE FELL FOR IT HOOK, LINE AND SINKER!

Penny had made the story up knowing that Linda couldn't say no to a challenge.

LINDA HAD NO IDEA THAT I'D GOT A MAP STUFFED UP MY JUMPER, I THOUGHT 'SHE'S BOUND TO SEE THE BULGE' BUT SHE DIDN'T.

STILL THE WHOLE TRICK WOULDN'T HAVE WORKED IF SHE KNEW THERE'D ALWAYS BEEN A CAVE UP HERE.

YOU TOOK YOUR TIME, I ALMOST GOT FED UP WAITING FOR YOU.

WELL EVEN THOUGH I KNEW THE WAY I HAD TO GIVE THE IMPRESSION I WAS LOST. WE DIDN'T COME STRAIGHT UP, WE HAD TO WANDER ABOUT A BIT FIRST.

Nick Heyward

The Flying Pickets

ARE YOU JUST A PRETTY FACE?

We hope not, clever girls should know all the slick beauty tricks too! See if you do — try our quiz!

1 You've run out of toothpaste but don't want to go out without brushing your teeth. As an emergency alternative you can use . . .
a) Soap?
b) A little salt sprinkled in water?
c) A splash of mouthwash on your toothbrush?

2 Your hair's a bit greasy but there's no time to wash it. You . . .
a) Dab a little cologne on your hairline to soak up the grease?
b) Run a bar of soap along your hairline to absorb the grease?
c) Shake a little talcum powder on to your hairbrush and gently brush it through your hair?

3 The kitchen cupboard could be just the place to find something to make your hair gleam. If you've got fair hair a few drops of (one of the following) in your final rinsing water is just the thing. Should you use . . .
a) Apple juice?
b) Lemon juice?
c) Vinegar?

4 If your hair's *dark* you should use . . .
a) Apple juice?
b) Lemon juice?
c) Vinegar?

5 For tired or puffy eyes there's no better natural remedy than relaxing for ten minutes with . . .
a) A slice of cucumber on each eye?
b) A slice of melon on each eye?
c) A slice of pear on each eye?

6 Your elbows look a bit grey and grimy. There's an instant solution. You press each one into . . .
a) Half an avocado?
b) Half a lemon?
c) Half a coconut?

7 You don't have/don't like mascara with fibres, but you do want to add a bit of volume to those lashes. You . . .
a) Dust the lashes with a little talcum powder before you put on your usual one light coat of mascara?
b) Horrify Mum and Dad by putting on as many coats of mascara as you can?
c) Horrify Mum and Dad by putting on as many coats as you can find — before the stuff dries?

8 Which of the following would you add to your bath every now and again if you were very health conscious . . .
a) Rose hip tea — it smells funny but is great for the skin?
b) Goat's milk — expensive but worth the trouble?
c) A couple of tablespoons of Mum's cooking salt?

9 You've had a boring day at school but want to liven up for the evening. What's the best way to get that extra energy and zip?
a) Eating a high-sugar snack?
b) Lying on the ground with your feet propped above your head for ten minutes?
c) Doing 30 minutes vigorous exercise?

10 Which of the following makes the best natural conditioner for just washed hair . . .
a) Beaten egg?
b) The white of an egg?
c) The yolk of an egg?

Kim Wilde

GOOD AS NEW

Got some dull and boring clothes in your wardrobe that you don't know what to do with? Or perhaps you've got some gear that's falling apart at the seams! If you have, then we've got plenty of ideas and tips on giving some of your clothes a complete new look!

Fed-up with that boring white blouse or plain old dress? Well, liven 'em up with a few clever extra touches . . .

Big, bright buttons sewn on the front of your blouse would certainly cheer it up. Even sew them on the sleeves or shoulders! The same goes for your dresses too. Most big stores sell eye-catching buttons that you can sew onto your clothes and transform your whole outfit with!

Want a pair of leg-warmers? Well, you could always cut the sleeves off an old jumper to make a pair! Just make sure you neaten the ends you've cut with some strong stitching, so that they don't unravel. You might even pick up some jumpers in a jumble sale for a few pence and make yourself lots of different coloured pairs.

Tying a piece of material round your head may sound strange, but it can look good. The messier it looks the better! Have a rummage round the fabric department of your local store and see if they have a few remnants going cheap.

If you're bored with the colour of a t-shirt, top or dress you can always change it! Dylon have got a great range of dyes — some to change the colour completely, some you use on shoes and even some you can just paint on for a special effect. Try them and see! Have a look at the instructions on the back of Dylon tins and bottles to see just what you can do with their dyes. Remember, though, that some fabrics are not suitable for dying. So be careful!

48

Always bear in mind that it's well worth a snoop around local jumble sales, Oxfam shops or even special shops that sell second-hand gear. You might just pick up a great bargain! But be warned — the chances are you'll have to wade through a lot of junk first! It's also well worth considering having a clothes swop party with your friends but make sure Mum approves first!

If you're really short of cash and you'd love a new sweater or cardie, why not unravel an old jumper to make up a new one? Just make sure you don't take Mum's best jumper to pieces! Again, local jumble sales or Oxfam shops are the best sources for old knits that you can re-cycle.

If you fancy a pair of fingerless gloves why not cut the fingers off an old pair — and we mean an *old* pair — not brand new ones Mum's just bought for you! Make sure you stitch the ragged ends thoroughly so you don't end up with frayed edgings that look messy!

Spandau Ballet

Gary Numan

Shakin' Stevens

Bedtime Stories

It's no fairytale that sleep is the best beauty treatment in town!

You may not realise it, but sleep is a very important part of your daily beauty routine and certainly one you shouldn't skimp.

There aren't any set rules about how much sleep you should get each night, but most people tend to need around eight hours or more. To find out how much you need, listen to your body's needs — it'll soon tell you what it wants, when it wants!

If you wake up each morning feeling listless and heavy-headed, you may need more sleep. Try to make yourself go to bed a bit earlier — you could be short-changing yourself!

LUCKY

If, on the other hand, you find yourself waking up early in the morning and not able to get back to sleep, why waste the day? Get up and enjoy yourself! You're one of those lucky people who only need a minimum of sleep.

Most of us can be lumped into two groups of sleepers — larks and owls.

The larks rise happily and cheerfully each morning, in contrast to the sleepy owls, who can hardly stagger out of bed. But when night comes, the owls get their own back. They're still raring to go, just when the larks are off to fill their hot water bottles!

If you're a light sleeper or have trouble dropping off, take time to prepare yourself before you lie down to sleep. Make sure there's no irritating noise that will keep you awake.

To make sure of a good night's rest, avoid eating just before you go to bed. Foods like cheese, apples and onions will definitely not help you sleep. However, a steaming hot drink like milk or Ovaltine will help you relax, just before you snuggle up to your favourite teddy!

And before you settle down for the night, don't skip your beauty routine. Make sure your skin is spotlessly clean and don't forget to brush your teeth. Then comb your hair right through to get rid of any uncomfortable tangles you might have.

COMFORTABLE

Whatever you wear in bed, make sure it's comfortable, if you tend to feel the cold, pyjamas are cosiest!

Don't wear anything that's too tight around the neck, or a long nightie that tangles round your legs and makes you feel as though you're tied up in knots! And in the Summer, when it's really hot, there's nothing wrong with sleeping in the raw!

Finally, if you find it hard to get to sleep, there's a lot to be said for counting sheep! But you could try letting the words of your favourite pop song run through your head. You'll almost be in John Taylor's arms as you drift off to sleep . . .

Sleeping *on your back* indicates a calm person who has no secrets from the world. You're not scared of anything or anyone and are content to take life as it comes.

Sleeping *on your stomach* is the sign of the ostrich. You want to bury your head in the invisible sands of your pillow. You don't like sleeping at all really, preferring your waking moments every time!

LOVEABLE

If you sleep *curled up* like a cat, it's because you want to avoid facing problems. However, you're warm, feminine and loveable, if sometimes a little too sensitive!

Sleeping *on your side* — and it doesn't matter which side — means you're peaceful and relaxed, but you don't like change or unpredictable behaviour in others.

If you sleep *diagonally across the bed,* you're a well-balanced person who's popular at work or at play — everybody's friend!

And, lastly, if you wake up with the bed in a mess, 'cos you've been *tossing and turning* all night, it means you're dreaming in your sleep, and living your life through your dreams!

Of course, as you're asleep you're not likely to know what position you finally doze off in, so you'll have to ask Mum to look in and check for you!

Sleeping Beauties

Believe it or not, the way you sleep says a great deal about you. Bet you never knew that! Read on and find out just what we mean!

Your Dreams And You

Most people dream for about two hours every night, though most of us can't remember one single dream when we wake up! But when you do remember them, what do they mean? Our dream dictionary will help you to interpret your dreams. . .

Angel — a disappointment
Arrow — one flying is a sign of success and happiness
Attic — a desire to start afresh
Baboon — a sign of mischief
Baby — this means riches
Badger — a sign of hard work

Ballet — a desire for the finer things in life
Beach — change from the ordinary
Bees — a good omen for prosperity
Boat — the return of a friend
Cabbage — a sign of birth
Cage — sympathy for a close friend
Candle — a wedding — if it's lighted
Cat — good luck
Dogs — a howling dog is a sign of danger
Eggs — this means profit
Elephant — unexpected help
Eyes — you attach importance to what people say and think
Fire — uneasiness
Fog — inability to make up your mind
Geese — a strong desire to roam
Honey — a sign of being lazy
Ice — skating shows a desire to find an easy solution to a problem
Ivy — this means good health
Jade — jealousy
Jewellery — good fortune
Kitten — children playing
Lace — a sign of anxiety
Leaves — peace and friendship
Lettuce — an indication of plenty
Magic — a change is about to occur
Money — good omen
Nails — riches or a windfall
Nurse — a good omen
Occult — forthcoming changes
Orange Blossom — marriage
Pearls — an indication of hard work
Pirates — a romantic phase in your life
Pyramid — curiosity
Queen — joy and prosperity
Rabbits — increase in the family
Railway — a journey
Rhubarb — good health
Satin — vanity
Stairs — ambition
Tears — these are an indication of pleasure
Thunder — fear of a forthcoming meeting
Waterlilies — a desire for the unobtainable
Yacht — a wishing for riches
Zoo — friendship and sympathy for others

A Home for Heartbreak

WELL, HOW DO I LOOK? I FEEL JUST LIKE A PENGUIN, DRESSED UP LIKE THIS!

YOU LOOK GREAT, DAD. REALLY SMART!

YOU DON'T MIND ME GOING OUT TONIGHT, DO YOU, LOVE? I COULDN'T REALLY MISS THE FIRM'S DO.

'COURSE I DON'T MIND.

NOT IN THE LEAST. MAYBE NOW HE'LL START ENJOYING HIMSELF. POOR DAD HASN'T HAD MUCH FUN SINCE MUM DIED.

THAT'S YOUR AUNT SHEILA AT THE DOOR. I'LL BE OFF THEN, LOVE.

HAVE A LOVELY TIME, DAD.

Vicky's aunt was only seven years older than her!

OKAY — WHERE'S THE BABY I'VE COME TO BABY SIT!

GIVE OVER, SHEILA — I'M ALMOST FOURTEEN. I'VE JUST FINISHED MY HOMEWORK. FANCY A GAME OF CARDS?

I'VE BROUGHT THE LATEST HOWARD JONES ROUND WITH ME, I BOUGHT IT TODAY.

GREAT, PUT IT ON.

YOUR DAD LOOKED NICE.

YES, HE DID, DIDN'T HE? D'YOU THINK ANYONE WILL FANCY HIM?

NOT MATCHMAKING, ARE YOU?

I LOVED MUM EVER SO MUCH, SHEILA, BUT I'D REALLY LIKE IT IF DAD FOUND SOMEONE AND GOT MARRIED AGAIN.

MAYBE YOU'LL GET YOUR WISH!

WHAT DO YOU MEAN? DO YOU KNOW SOMETHING I DON'T KNOW? COME ON, SHEILA!

UH—UH — MUM'S THE WORD!

OOOH! I COULD KILL YOU SOMETIMES!

58

STILL AWAKE?

YES, DAD.

DID YOU HAVE A NICE TIME?

YES, VICKY, I HAD A SUPER TIME. AND THAT ISN'T QUITE ALL, BUT I DON'T KNOW HOW TO SAY IT. . .

SAY WHAT, DAD? DID YOU MEET SOMEONE?

WELL, NOT EXACTLY MEET . . .I'VE KNOWN, ER, KAREN FOR THE LAST YEAR. SHE WORKS AT BENTLEYS, TOO.

I LIKE HER A LOT, VICKY, BUT I DON'T WANT YOU TO THINK BADLY OF ME. IT'S ONLY THREE YEARS SINCE YOUR MUM DIED, AFTER ALL.

BUT MUM WOULD HAVE WANTED YOU TO BE HAPPY, DAD, AND SO DO I.

I'M GLAD YOU'VE MET SOMEONE NICE. . .I REALLY AM.

THANKS, LOVE. YOU'VE TAKEN A WEIGHT OFF MY MIND.

SO WHEN'S THE WEDDING?

EH? THAT'S JUMPING THE GUN A BIT, ISN'T IT?

But it wasn't. After that, Vicky's dad couldn't stop talking about Karen!

SHE'S DIVORCED, VICKY, AND SOMETHING ELSE I HAVEN'T TOLD YOU — SHE'S GOT A DAUGHTER ABOUT YOUR AGE, MAYBE A LITTLE YOUNGER.

BUT THAT'S GREAT DAD! TELL ME ALL ABOUT HER...

THAT'S GREAT. I JUST KNOW EVERYTHING'S GOING TO WORK OUT FINE!

I THINK IT'S SERIOUS, SHEILA — I THINK DAD AND KAREN ARE GOING TO GET MARRIED!

HAVE YOU MET JOSY YET?

NO — AND I'M A BIT NERVOUS.

IT'LL BE OKAY, ALTHOUGH KAREN TENDS TO BE A BIT OVER-PROTECTIVE BECAUSE OF EVERYTHING. BUT JOSY'S REALLY NICE.

YOUR DAD HAS TOLD YOU ABOUT HER, I SUPPOSE?

YES, I FEEL SO SORRY FOR HER....

But, although Vicky had been warned...

...seeing Josy's wheelchair was still a shock!

HELLO, YOU MUST BE VICKY. THANKS FOR ASKING ME ROUND.

HELLO.

SHE MUST EVEN HATE IT THAT I CAN HELP HER WITH THE DISHES, BUT JOSY CAN'T!

IT HASN'T BEEN TOO BAD FOR ME — WORSE FOR MUM. IT'S MADE HER VERY ANGRY INSIDE, ABOUT OTHER PEOPLE. I'M SO GLAD SHE'S MET YOUR DAD.

THAT'S IT — IT FEELS LIKE SHE'S ANGRY WITH ME FOR BEING WELL AND HEALTHY WHEN HER OWN DAUGHTER ISN'T!

I KNOW SHE LOVES DAD AND SHE PROBABLY DOESN'T MEAN TO BE THE WAY SHE IS WITH ME, BUT WHAT CAN I DO TO CHANGE THINGS?

DAD. . .IF ONLY JOSY COULD WALK AGAIN — I'D GIVE ANYTHING!

BETTER FACE UP TO IT, LOVE — HER MUM THINKS THAT MAY NEVER HAPPEN.

But one morning about a fortnight later. . .

VICKY, I'M SO EXCITED! I FELT SOMETHING IN MY LEGS LAST NIGHT. IT'S STILL THERE. I HAVEN'T TOLD MUMMY, THOUGH, SHE GETS SO FUNNY.

BUT ARE YOU SURE?

'COURSE I'M SURE. VICKY. . .PLEASE, WOULD YOU HELP ME GET OUT OF BED?

I — I DON'T KNOW, JOSY — WHAT IF YOU SHOULD FALL? DON'T YOU WANT TO WAIT?

63

64

STARSCOPE!

How should you pick your mates? Will your best friend stay your closest mate, or will she abandon you for someone else? The answer's in the stars!

CAPRICORN

You're steady, methodical and practical. You're not keen on doing mad things, preferring to think things through rather than get carried away on a crazy idea. And the strange thing is, you're always right in the end!

What you enjoy:- Reading, and playing 'thinking' games like chess and backgammon.

Your favourite friends:- Virgoans, with their love of order, will appeal to your slow, steady and cautious nature.

Who'll drive you mad? Aquarians! They're just a bit too crazy for your liking! You hate rushing around, so quiet types are for you!

AQUARIUS

You're wild, crazy and totally original. You get bored really easily and tend to get on with loads of people. Friends love you because you're such fun to be with — but they get a bit fed up with your unreliable ways!

What you enjoy: Unusual things like tap dancing and writing poetry capture your interest. But you soon get bored with what you're doing!

Your favourite friends:- Anyone at all! You tend to prefer loads of not-so-close friends to really special mates.

Who'll drive you mad? Beware the Scorpio pal — she's a bit too possessive and demanding for your liking!

PISCES

You're definitely the dreamer of the zodiac! You avoid the harsh realities of life, preferring to lock yourself away in a world where you can pretend to be anyone from Jayne Torvill to Simon Le Bon's girlfriend. You're gentle, loving, and don't like trouble.

What you enjoy:- Drawing, writing — anything artistic!

Your favourite friends:- Cancer, another gentle, peace-loving sign, will team up well with you.

Who'll drive you mad? Capricorn. Their practical, down to earth nature will forever be shattering those all important daydreams of yours!

ARIES

You're loud, brash and very bossy! Sometimes your determination makes you forget other people's feelings, but you can be very nice too, when it suits you!

What you enjoy:- A hobby where you can prove what a good leader you are, like guides. But you can be very disorganised, too!

Your favourite friends:- Sagittarians tend to tolerate your bossy nature the best! Who'll drive you mad? Leo people, definitely! You'll be forever arguing with them over who's in charge. It wouldn't hurt you to step down for once, but you won't, will you?!

TAURUS

Slow, steady, plodding — that's good old Taurus! But while these may seem like bad points, they also mean that you like to stick at things and you manage to get things done when other people would just give up!

What you enjoy:- You like hobbies you can do at home, like reading or drawing. Outdoor activities aren't for you!

Your favourite friends:- You get on well with that other home loving sign, Cancer. Capricorns also appeal to your slow, steady nature.

Who'll drive you mad? Aquarians! They're just too quick for you to keep up with! Also Leo — you don't like being told what to do!

GEMINI

No-one ever knows where they are with you! One minute you're up in the air, the next you're down in the dumps! Because of that you tend to be interesting to have around — but not very reliable!

What you enjoy:- Lively, active-type hobbies like roller skating, swimming or athletics.

Your favourite friends:- You'll keep an Aquarian pal guessing — and that's just the way she likes it!

Who'll drive you mad? Slow, dreamy Pisces people find it hard to keep up with you — and that could drive you crazy after a while. You're not the most tolerant of people!

CANCER

Gentle, passive and peace loving, that's you! You'd do anything to avoid an argument, preferring the quiet life every time. But if someone does wind you up, it takes you a very long time to calm down again!
What you enjoy:- Cooking. Home-loving Cancerians really like their food!

Your favourite friends:- Dreamy Pisces pals will get on well with you — although you might not make a very dynamic duo! But your friendship will be trouble-free if nothing else!
Who'll drive you mad? Bossy Aries mates will try to run your life for you — which you won't like one little bit!

LEO

Fiery tempered, quick to take offence — that's you! But you're also very good at making decisions and like to get things done — people look to you for ideas and inspiration!
What you enjoy:- 'Leading' activities like guides or camping — anything where you can feel important!
Your favourite friends:- Well-balanced Librans who'll cope with your occasional bossiness without a murmur!
Who'll drive you mad? You won't get on too well with an Aries person — you'll drive each other mad. Scorpio people might be a bit too hot-tempered for you, too.

VIRGO

You're the perfectionist of the zodiac chart. You demand everyone to fall into line with you. And if something's not quite right, you soon let everyone know about it!
What you enjoy:- Hobbies that require a lot of patience and are complex — Rubik's Cube type puzzles, mega-sized jigsaw puzzles or knitting complex patterns.
Your favourite friends:- You'd suit a Capricorn friend — you both share a love of order and tidiness.
Who'll drive you mad? Aquarians with their untidy habits would really make tempers rise and lead to rows!

LIBRA

You're calm, well-balanced — and a bit flirtatious when you want to be! People warm to you because you can be very sweet and charming. But underneath all that sweetness lies a very determined streak!
What you enjoy:- You love creating pretty things, so you probably enjoy knitting, embroidery or painting.
Your favourite friends:- A peace loving Piscean would appreciate your gentle ways — and they'd let you get your own way — most of the time!
Who'll drive you mad? Hard-headed Capricorns who'll see through your wily ways and stand up to you!

SCORPIO

You're hot tempered and fiery! You can be very jealous and possessive, which frightens people off. But you can also be a very good friend in times of trouble and stress.
What you enjoy:- You're very good at concentrating and like pastimes that demand a lot of skill and concentration, like chess or even mountaineering!
Your favourite friends:- Capricorns will help calm you down occasionally, which is what you need.
Who'll drive you mad? Leo and Aries friends will try to boss you around, while Aquarians won't stay around long enough for your liking!

SAGITTARIUS

You're lively and full of energy! Your head's always full of new and exciting ideas, which can make you a bit hard to keep up with! You don't tend to stay in the same place more than five minutes!
What you enjoy:- Something that really taxes that lively brain of yours, like crossword puzzles!

Your favourite friends:- Aquarian mates will share your interest in everything new and interesting.
Who'll drive you mad? Slow, steady Taureans will drag you down and stop you getting on with life. And you won't like that one little bit! Steer clear of them and have fun!

ULTRAQUIZ

1. What is Marilyn's real name?

2. Who is The Riddler who enjoys a bit of Human Racing?

3. What day did Duran Duran have a new moon on?

4. Two members of Heaven 17 were once half of which other famous and talented pop band?

5. What is the name of Spandau Ballet's drummer?

6. Whose chart-topping album was called 'You Broke My Heart In 17 Places'?

7. What is Nick Rhodes real name?

8. Who is the odd one out here, and why? Think hard!
a) Paul McCartney
b) Boy George
c) Mick Jagger

9. Which city do Frankie Goes To Hollywood come from?

10. Who had hits with the following songs:
a) Talking In Your Sleep?
b) Sweet Dreams (Are Made Of This)?
c) Wake Me Up Before You Go Go?

11. What is the name of Culture Club's drummer?

12. Who recently Just Called To Say I Love You?

13. Captain Sensible has enjoyed several solo hits, but he is also a

Think you know it all when it comes to pop, do you? Well, get your thinking caps on and test yourself on this lot!

long-standing member with which famous band?

14. Who is Christopher Hamill better known as?

15. Which pop star starred in his own film, Purple Rain?

16. What is Sade's surname?

17. Which of the three Thompson Twins was the founder member?

18. Paul Young is now successful in a solo career, but can you name the eight-piece band he used to sing with (Clue: they were a right earful!)

19. Can you name both of the backing singers with Wham!?

20. What was the name of the Paul McCartney film that also starred Ringo Starr and Tracey Ullman?

21. Who are Holly, Paul, Nasher, Ped and Mark better known as?

22. Who had hits with Dancing With Tears In My Eyes, and Loves Great Adventure?

23. Who said he'd Like To Get To Know You Well?

24. Who bounced back into the charts after a long absence with Never Ending Story?

25. Which Radio 1 DJ was the first to ban Relax?

ANSWERS

1. Peter Robinson.

2. Nik Kershaw

3. Monday.

4. Human League.

5. John Keeble

6. Tracey Ullman

7. Nick Bates.

8. Boy George. He's the only one who hasn't recorded a duet with Michael Jackson.

9. Liverpool.

10. Bucks Fizz.

    Eurythmics.

    Wham!

11. Jon Moss

12. Stevie Wonder.

13. The Damned.

14. Limahl.

15. Prince.

16. Adu.

17. Tom Bailey.

18. The Q-Tips.

19. Shirley and Pepsi.

20. Give My Regards To Broad Street.

21. Frankie Goes To Hollywood.

22. Ultravox.

23. Howard Jones.

24. Limahl.

25. Mike Read.

ARE YOU GROWN UP...

OR AN OVER-GROWN KID?

It's the same old story . . . some people can't wait to be adults, others just want to stay kids. So, read on and you'll find out which is true of you!

1. If your mum sends you to bed it's because:
a) *Coronation Street* has just finished and it's time you were up there sound asleep?
b) It's 2 in the morning, you've just come in from a wild party and it's time you were up there?
c) You're covered in nasty red spots — and it looks like measles!?

2. If you were piling on the make-up it'd mean:
a) Another late night party was about to begin?
b) You'd got that part in the school play you wanted?
c) Your elder sister was letting you play 'beauticians' on her again!?

3. The last time you went to a film you were accompanied by:
a) An adult — with all these PGs you think it's best?
b) Your kid sister — you were too embarrassed to turn up at *101 Dalmations* on your own!?
c) A minder — it's pretty rough at the sort of cinemas you frequent!?

4. You always eat at McDonalds because:
a) That's what everybody in *Girl* does!?
b) That's where the boys go?
c) Ronald McDonald always has time — and a free balloon — for you, his best customer!?

5. Your hero is:
a) *Roland Rat* — he's funny and cuddly?
b) *John Taylor* — he's a honey and cuddly?
c) *Brer Rabbit* — he's a bunny and cuddly!?

6. Your ideal birthday present would be:
a) 'My Little Pony'?
b) A date with *John Taylor?*
c) 'My Little Pony' — autographed by *John Taylor!?*

7. You've still got your Rupert Bear annuals. Do you:
a) Read them every night before you go to sleep?
b) Flick through them very, very occasionally?
c) Never look at them — you keep meaning to give them away?

8. You're out hunting for new clothes. Do you:
a) Buy the same sort of gear you always do?
b) Buy whatever's in fashion?
c) Buy the same sort of outfit your best mate goes for?

YOUR SCORE

1.	a) 0	b) 10	c) 5
2.	a) 10	b) 5	c) 5
3.	a) 0	b) 5	c) 10
4.	a) 5	b) 10	c) 0
5.	a) 5	b) 10	c) 0
6.	a) 0	b) 10	c) 5
7.	a) 0	b) 5	c) 10
8.	a) 0	b) 5	c) 10

Mostly 0's:
It's strictly 'small talk' for you, you're scarcely out of babygrows! It's wonderful to keep alive the best aspects of childhood, but you're taking it to extremes. You can be mature without missing out on the fun. Try it and see!

Mostly 5's:
No kidding — you've got it about right! You aren't so keen to grow up that you're missing out on being young, but you've outgrown the need to be the centre of attention. The 'kid' will still be with you at 95!

Mostly 10's
You're getting on . . . everyone's nerves, mostly! It's about time you acted your age and realised that pretending to be grown-up is just a childish game! Relax, most adults are kids at heart!

IF YOU NEED HELP ...

I'M BEING BULLIED

I'm so unhappy. You see, there's a girl at school who's making my life a misery. She keeps picking on me and calling me nasty names.

What can I do about her?

Girl Fan, Scotland.

Bullies are nasty people who love to upset those weaker than themselves. The best thing you can do is to ignore this girl because once she sees she's not getting to you anymore she'll soon stop trying and leave you alone.

However, if things get unbearable, you must confide in a teacher. She'll be able to put a stop to this girl's nasty ways.

It's hard to understand why people do like to be bullies, it's usually because they're unhappy themselves. You should really pity this girl — although I know it must be difficult.

THEY'RE TOO STRICT

Please help! My parents are so strict. All my friends have boyfriends and go to discos — but I'm not allowed. All they want me to do is study, even at weekends.

I feel so unhappy.

Alison, London.

Obviously your parents have your best interests at heart, but I can understand how you must feel.

Try to sit down and talk to them, compromise in some way, both sides need to give and take a little. Suggest that if all your homework is done you should have a weekend off.

Don't expect too much at once, though, just be patient and gradually they'll come round.

I DON'T KNOW HOW TO KISS

I've been asked out by lots of boys but I've always said no. You see, I don't know how to kiss and I'm frightened of making a fool of myself with them.

How do you kiss?

Lisa, London.

Kissing is something that comes naturally and it's impossible for me to describe it to you. I can understand you feeling nervous, because the first kiss is always a bit awkward. However, next time you're asked make sure you go — you may not even get kissed at the end of the night, so all the worrying will have been for nothing! But if he does want to kiss you, relax, close your eyes and everything will come naturally!

WHEN WILL I START?

I'm so worried because I'm 14 and haven't started my periods yet. All my friends have and I feel like the odd one out.

Louise, Somerset.

Please don't worry. There's no set age for you to start your periods — some girls start as early as 10 while others don't start until they're 18. It's all to do with your own particular body, and your own cycle.

Yours will start as soon as your body is ready for them.

There's nothing abnormal about you at all, so stop worrying.

I'M SO FAT!

I'm 13, very fat *and* spotty. I've tried several creams with no success and I've tried dieting too, but never seem to lose any weight.

What can I do?

Mandy, Liverpool.

It's very common for young girls to have teenage spots as well as puppy fat — it's all part of growing up!

But for now you could try cutting out greasy foods and chocolate which are high in calories, and bad for your skin.

If you fancy a nibble, try a piece of fruit and eat more vegetables, as they are low in calories and contain plenty of vitamins and protein which will give you a healthier looking skin too.

MUM'S A PROBLEM

Please help! I am really fed-up and worried.

I think it's time I started wearing a bra but I just can't talk to Mum about it. She keeps telling me I've got bags of time before I need to wear one.

My breasts have started developing and the other girls at school are noticing when we change for P.E.

Juliet, Wimbledon.

First of all, you must sit down and talk to your mum. Tell her how embarrassed you are in the changing room and that your school mates are noticing.

Lots of bra manufacturers bring out bras specially made for girls who are just beginning to develop. They give a small amount of support and will make you feel much more comfortable.

MEET MR. BAILEY!

To say that the Thompson Twins have worked hard for their success would be putting it mildly!

"We've even spent the last three years working on Christmas Day," Tom said.

"We always seem to be recording a new album around that time of year. Not that missing the festivities really bothers me. It's not that I'm a misery or anything, it's just that I'm a vegetarian so Christmas dinner and all that doesn't mean much to me."

Tom reckons that the trouble with being so busy is that you miss out on your mates.

"I haven't got any friends left from the days before I joined the band," he admitted.

"I just don't have time to visit people. I try to have two or three friends in each major city. But sometimes when I get into somewhere like London and I feel like going out, I suddenly realise that there really aren't many people I know to ask!"

Probably his best friends are Alannah and Joe.

"We're very, very close," he reckons. "We spend so much time together so it's natural really.

"People are surprised to hear how little we argue, although Alannah's temper has knocked the wind out of Joe and me on more than one occasion!

"But I know that if ever something's troubling me, I can turn to one of those two and they'll help me sort it out. I do the same for them too, of course."

LOVERS

Tom doesn't have many girlfriends either. He and Alannah were lovers for a time. But not anymore.

"There's no-one serious in my life, which is fine by me because I don't ever want to get married. I plan to stay single because getting married is such an old fashioned and silly thing to do.

"I would never go out with a girl who didn't share my views on the subject because it only leads to trouble in the end.

"That's why Alannah and I got on so well together. She is an independent career woman, with her own life to lead. She doesn't want to get tied down in a heavy relationship and that's why we stayed together for so long. We just drifted together really and drifted apart.

"When we eventually split up there were no hard feelings on either side. We'd had a good time and that's all that mattered. Now we're the best of mates.

"So as far as I'm concerned when it comes to marriage you can count me out!"

Mmm — someone may persuade him yet! And in the meantime?

"The band is based in Paris which I like because we're not too well known there. Even so, there's always a place in my heart for England! We'd miss you otherwise!"

Glad to hear it!

QUICK QUIZ

1. Fill in the missing words from these Thompson Twins singles.
a) ------ Doctor
b) Hold Me ---
c) --- Your ----- On Me
2. How many members were in the original Thompson Twins line-up?
3. Where is Alannah from?

4. Joe worked for the original Thompson Twin line-up before he joined the band. Doing what?

ANSWERS

1. a) Doctor b) Hold Me Now
c) Lay Your Hands On Me
2. Seven 3. New Zealand 4. He was a roadie.

FULL NAME: Tom Bailey
DATE OF BIRTH: 18th January, 1957.
PLACE OF BIRTH: Chesterfield.
PRESENT HOME: Paris.
PREVIOUS JOBS: Rubbish collector, ice cream man and teacher.

FAVOURITE FOOD: Vegetarian.
LIKES: Alannah and Joe.
DISLIKES: Having no privacy.
AMBITION: To carry on having the fantastic opportunities we've had over the last few years. Otherwise I just want to be

Can't decide what to wear?
Don't know what sort of clothes
suit you best? Well believe it or
not, the answer's in the stars —
your zodiac sign reveals all!

It's in the

Aries
(MAR 21/APR 20)

You've got a pretty strong character so don't be afraid to dress in bold and striking colours and styles. If you want to wear something pretty way out go ahead — 'cos you can carry it off! You're always the first to wear the latest styles and like your mates to follow suit.

Taurus
(APR 21/MAY 21)

Taurans can be passive and gentle so aim for gear that's smart and sophisticated. Bright colours aren't your scene at all, and wouldn't suit your personality. Wear soft, pastel colours that suit your gentle personality — you'll look just amazing!

Gemini
(MAY 22/JUNE 21)

Geminis are always on the go. You're restless and you like plenty of variety in your life. Why not wear track-suits? They're loose and comfortable — and you'll knock 'em for six!

Cancer
(JUNE 22/JULY 23)

You're one of the lucky signs that can wear just about anything. There's no ruling planet in your sign to suggest anything but to just go out and buy whatever takes your fancy! Just make sure it suits you before you take the plunge and splash out on something that costs a bomb!

Leo
(JULY 24/AUG 23)

You're another person with a powerful personality so don't be afraid to wear clothes and colours that will make you stand out in the crowd. Bright pinks and reds are just your sort of thing — you look great in them!

Virgo
(AUG 24/SEPT 23)

You're a very feminine girl so when you're buying clothes, aim for gentle pinks and blues in soft baggy lines. Really strong clothes with a military type look just aren't you!

Libra
(SEPT 24/OCT 23)

You're the one star sign that loves to dress beautifully! You don't spare much expense when it comes to clothes, do you? Well seeing that you look pretty good dressed up you might as well carry on indulging yourself. Keep an eye on your bank balance though!

Scorpio
(OCT 24/NOV 22)

You've got to always wear stuff that's really fashionable. You're a girl that follows every trend and fashion fad, whether it suits you or not. You'd rather be dead than seen in last year's gear!

Sagittarius
(NOV 23/DEC 21)

The chances are you love sport so, like Geminis, why not grab yourself some colourful and comfy tracksuits? You'll look like a million dollars in them and keep fit at the same time!

Capricorn
(DEC 22/JAN 20)

Seeing as you're pretty neat and tidy you're the sort of girl who can wear lots of pretty tops and blouses. You're terrific when it comes to keeping your clothes in good order, so plenty of accessories are just up your street. They'll give an individual touch to whatever you wear.

Aquarius
(JAN 21/FEB 19)

You're pretty unconventional — you hate sticking to rules and regulations! So why not wear clothes to match your personality and go for stuff that's really different? Jumble sales and Oxfam shops would be good hunting grounds for you — and cheap too!

Pisces
(FEB 20/MAR 20)

You're one of the most emotional signs in the Zodiac. Go for pretty, smart clothes. Little bows, pretty ribbons and generally feminine gear is what looks best on Pisces!

The Girl Guide To Natural Beauty.

The shops are packed with expensively-wrapped beauty products, but did you know that it's no trouble at all to make your own at home for far less money? Try out our natural recipes with a mate — they're mouthwateringly-simple and fun to do!

BANANA FACE MASK

1 ripe banana
2 tsps honey
4 tsps single cream

Mash the banana thoroughly and add the honey and cream. Spread the mixture quickly over your face, avoiding the delicate skin around your eyes. Leave for 15 minutes before removing. You'll notice the difference immediately — your skin should feel wonderfully clean and smooth — and smell of bananas!

REFRESHING LEMON SKIN TONIC

½ lemon
½ pt water

Extract juice from lemon and add to water, then simply splash your face with the tonic. You'll find it's a great start to the day!

MINT AND YOGHURT MOISTURISING MASK

½ 5oz pot of natural yoghurt
6 mint leaves

Chop the mint leaves finely and add to yoghurt. Mix together well. Spread evenly over face and neck and leave for ten minutes before washing off.

PINEAPPLE CUTICLE SOFTENER

2 tbsps fresh pineapple juice
2 tbsps egg yolk
½ tsp cider vinegar

Mix the ingredients together and soak your fingernails in it for half an hour, before removing cuticles.

COUNTRY HERB BATH

Take a selection of herbs such as lavender, mint, parsley, rosemary, thyme and bay leaves and fill a muslin bag. Hang this from the hot water tap when you have your bath and, as the water runs through the bag, the herbs' soothing properties will be released. Just lie back and soak up their natural goodness!

ORANGE FACE TONIC

½ orange (sliced)
¼ lemon
1 tbsp castor sugar
1 cup skimmed milk

Heat all the ingredients in a pan until nearly at boiling point. Leave to cool and sieve. This refreshing skin tonic will keep in the fridge for at least a couple of days.

APPLE MASK

1 peeled apple
½ tsp single cream
1 tbsp honey
1 tbsp ground oatmeal

Mash apple thoroughly in cream and stir in the honey and the oatmeal. Apply over face and neck evenly and leave on for ten minutes. Rinse off with luke-warm water and pat face gently with a dry towel.

ALMOND HAIR CONDITIONER

1 tsp almond oil
1 tsp dried rosemary
A little warm water

Mix ingredients together and rub the mixture into the ends of your damp hair. Leave on for ten minutes before rinsing your hair thoroughly.

LEMON AND HONEY PICK-YOU-UP

Juice of 1 lemon
1 tbsp honey
Water

Add lemon juice and honey to a glass of boiling water. Sip slowly. The ideal drink if you're suffering the miseries of a Winter cold!

HERBAL FEET TREAT!

Boil a selection of dried herbs in enough water for a footbath for ten minutes. Strain off herbal water, adding ¼ tsp of mustard powder to help stimulate circulation. Allow to cool slightly and soak feet in warm mixture for 15 minutes. You'll be doing tired feet a favour! A terrific tonic if you've been trudging round the shops or raving it up at the disco!

Michael Jackson

Heaven 17

Nik Kershaw

WHY NOT? I CAN DO AS I LIKE. MRS. MARCH SAYS IT'S ALL RIGHT TO DO IT. I **LIKE** HURTING THINGS.

WHAT A HORRID GIRL!

YOU CAN'T ORDER ME ABOUT. I'LL PULL YOU TO PIECES, TOO IF YOU'RE NOT CAREFUL.

Then, as Prue passed the sunken crypt.

MR. QUIST'S HOARDING — IT'S BEEN SMASHED! WAS THAT ANYTHING TO DO WITH THE KNOCKING AND HAMMERING I HEARD FROM HERE LAST NIGHT?

Cautiously she peeped into the murk of the crypt —

SOMEONE WAS HERE LAST NIGHT — OVER HALF THE SKULLS ARE MISSING!

RUFUS DOGGETT STOLE SOME OUT OF THE CRYPT BEFORE. PERHAPS HE'S BEEN HERE AGAIN. I — I MUST PUT MY MIND AT REST — I'LL GO AND SEE HIM.

And so —

HE SELLS SKULLS TO THE ARISTOCRACY — AS ORNAMENTS. IT — IT'S DISGUSTING!

AH, MISS PRUDENCE. COME BACK FOR YOUR PRESENT YOUR FATHER WOULDN'T LET YOU TAKE?

HERE YOU ARE. I KEPT IT SPECIAL!

N — NO THANK YOU. WHERE ARE THE OTHER SKULLS?

ALL BOUGHT AND PAID FOR, MISS. ALL GONE OUT TO THE GENTRY WHO CAN'T GET ENOUGH OF THEM, PLUS AN HONEST TRADESMAN OR TWO. I'M REDUCED TO PAINTING INN SIGNBOARDS. THIS HERE'S FOR THE COLLYNGWOOD ARMS.

THE SAME COLLYNGWOODS THAT LIE BURIED IN FATHER'S CHURCH?

AND THE SAME THAT HAD THE EVIL SIR CLIVE FOR THE LAST OF THEIR LINE — MAY HIS NAME BE FOREVER CURSED.

WHY DO YOU SAY THAT?

'COS HE TERRORISED LONDON. HE WAS THE LONDON WITCH-FINDER. HIM AND THAT YOUNG DEVIL THAT HELPED HIM. SENT HUNDREDS TO THEIR DEATH THEY DID — OLD WOMEN, YOUNG GIRLS. STANDS TO REASON THEY COULDN'T ALL BE WITCHES BUT THOSE TWO CREATURES MADE 'EM ALL CONFESS NEVERTHELESS.

WHEN THOSE TWO DEVILS WAS TOOK BY PLAGUE 'TWAS THE GOOD GOD AT WORK. AND IF THERE'S WITCHES STILL ABOUT THEY WORK IN SECRET IN THE DARK.

WITCHES? CAN IT BE WITCHES THAT TROUBLE THE CHURCH? BUT FATHER ALWAYS SAID SUCH TALK WAS FOOLISH!

Prue walked thoughtfully beside the river for a long time. Then she bumped into Israel Quist the sexton.

I AIN'T SEEN NO GIRL, MISS!

ANY SIGN OF THAT GIRL MRS. MARCH HAS BROUGHT HERE, MR. QUIST?

I WAS HOPING YOU MIGHT BE ABLE TO TELL ME WHERE SHE CAME FROM. SHE SEEMS TO BE AN ORPHAN. DO YOU KNOW A FAMILY CALLED WENDOVER? SHE IS LUCY WENDOVER –

THAT'S NO SORT OF JOKE FOR A YOUNG LADY LIKE YOU TO BE MAKIN', MISS.

A JOKE? BUT I SPEAK THE TRUTH.

THEN YOU'D BEST FOLLOW ME.

LOOK THERE, YOUNG MISS PRUDENCE.

BUT HOW IS IT POSSIBLE? THIS MEANS THAT LUCY DIED OVER FIFTY YEARS AGO!

IN MEMORY OF OUR DAUGHTER LUCY WENDOVER Born May 1600 Taken from us August 1613

BUT IT CAN'T BE THE SAME LUCY WENDOVER, MR. QUIST! THE ONE ON THE GRAVESTONE DIED OVER 50 YEARS AGO!

MAYBE – AND MAYBE NOT. BUT THERE HAVE BEEN NO MORE WENDOVERS ROUND THESE PARTS SINCE LUCY MET HER MAKER.

BUT PERHAPS YOU IMAGINED THIS GIRL, MISS PRUDENCE. 'TIS POSSIBLE TO SEE STRANGE SHAPES IN THE MIST. DONE IT MYSELF.

I'D BETTER NOT TELL HIM I'VE MET HER IN THE HOUSE – FACE TO FACE.

IF I WERE SUPERSTITIOUS I'D BELIEVE LUCY WAS SOME KIND OF GHOST. BUT THAT'S FOOLISHNESS –

WAIT! DIDN'T LUCY HERSELF SAY SHE DIDN'T KNOW WHERE SHE CAME FROM? THAT SHE'D BEEN 'CALLED'? AND WHAT WAS MRS. MARCH UP TO THAT NIGHT WHEN I SAW HER UP HERE AMONG THE GRAVES?

Inside the rectory –

LUCY – I WANT TO SPEAK TO YOU. LUCY – YOU THERE?

THAT'S FUNNY – SHE DOESN'T SEEM TO BE ANYWHERE IN THE HOUSE.

AH, MRS. MARCH. I WANT AN EXPLANATION. JUST WHO IS THIS LUCY WENDOVER?

LUCY? A DEAR SWEET CHILD. TAKEN AWAY MOST CRUELLY SHE WAS. BUT BACK NOW. JUST AS WE SHALL ALL BE BACK SOON TO TAKE OUR REVENGE.

WE? WHO ARE 'WE'? WHAT ARE YOU TALKING ABOUT?

SHE WON'T ANSWER ME – SHE JUST STANDS THERE LIKE A STATUE. IT – IT FRIGHTENS ME. WHAT'S GOING ON HERE?

Then in Prue's own room –

LUCY! WHAT ARE YOU DOING HERE?

I THOUGHT IT WOULD BE FUN TO SLEEP IN YOUR NICE WARM BED TONIGHT. I FEEL THE COLD SO TERRIBLY, YOU SEE.

BUT WAIT — THERE IS A STRANGER HERE! THAT IS FORBIDDEN — WE MUST SEEK OUT THE STRANGER —

I — I MUST GET AWAY —

But then in her headlong flight —

AAARGH!

As Prue pulled herself up on a gravestone —

RIP

IN MEMORY OF PRUDENCE SYLVESTER DIED AUGUST 23 1666

OH, NO — LOOK! THAT GRAVESTONE — IT'S GOT MY NAME ON IT. AND — AND TOMORROW'S DATE!

THE CHURCH IS IN DARKNESS NOW . . . SHE MUST HAVE TAKEN MY POOR SICK FATHER BACK INTO THE HOUSE.

CAN MRS. MARCH REALLY BE A WITCH? FATHER ALWAYS SAID SUCH THINGS WERE PURE SUPERSTITION. BUT NOW I'M NOT SO SURE —

TH — THAT STRANGE CEREMONY WITH THE SKULLS IN THE CHURCH — IT — IT FRIGHTENED ME.

THOSE PEOPLE ARE FATHER'S MOST LOYAL PARISHIONERS. WHAT'S THE TROUBLE? WHY ARE THEY CONGREGATING AT THE CHURCH DOOR?

This church is shut to worshippers.

Parson Sylvester.

OH, NO!

Angrily Prue tore down the notice and hurried into the house —

YOU! THIS IS YOUR DOING, MRS. MARCH!

'TIS THE MASTER'S SIGNATURE, I DO BELIEVE!

FATHER — DID YOU SIGN THIS NOTICE?

FATHER! ARE YOU — ARE YOU WELL? DO YOU HEAR ME? FATHER — PLEASE SPEAK TO ME!

THE SKULLS . . . THE SKULLS . . .

87

WHAT ABOUT THE SKULLS? REMEMBER YOU LEFT HOME TO SEEK ADVICE ABOUT THEM. WHAT DO YOU KNOW? PLEASE TELL ME...

THE SKULLS... HORRIBLE!... THEY'RE COMING FOR ME — FOR EVERYONE!... AAARGH!

Worried sick, Prue rushed to fetch Doctor Tobias —

HE SOUNDS DELIRIOUS... LIKE HE'S GOT A FEVER. WE'LL SOON PUT THAT RIGHT.

PRAY HEAVEN YOU CAN, DOCTOR. BUT I FEAR IT IS NOT AS SIMPLE AS YOU THINK.

As the doctor examined Parson Sylvester —

HAVE YOU NO WORK, MISTRESS MARCH?

PLENTY, MISS PRUDENCE. 'TWILL NOT BE DONE FOR A LITTLE WHILE YET, THOUGH.

DOCTOR! YOU LOOK WORRIED — WHAT'S WRONG? WHAT AILS FATHER?

I — I HAVE SEEN A CASE LIKE THIS ONCE BEFORE — WHEN A WITCH PUT A CURSE ON A POOR WOMAN.

ARE — ARE YOU TELLING ME FATHER IS UNDER SOME SORT OF SPELL?

YES, CHILD — THAT'S THE SAD TRUTH. AND THERE IS NO MEDICINE I CAN GIVE HIM. BUT THERE IS ONE HOPE. PRAY FOR ME, CHILD.

WH — WHATEVER DID HE MEAN? BUT I WISH HIM GODSPEED. POOR FATHER'S LIFE DEPENDS ON HIM —

Quist, the gravedigger, looked grim.

SHOULDN'T HAVE LET HIM GO, MISS PRUDENCE. WITCH HUNTING IS A DANGEROUS BUSINESS — AS SIR CLIVE COLLYNGWOOD FOUND OUT.

BUT WE MUST DO SOMETHING MR. QUIST. WE CAN'T LET POOR FATHER DIE. AND WE CAN'T LET MRS. MARCH GET AWAY WITH IT... COME, I WANT TO SHOW YOU SOMETHING.

STRANGE. THERE WAS A HEADSTONE HERE WITH MY NAME AND DATE OF DEATH ON IT — TODAY'S DATE!

NOTHING OF THE KIND HERE, MISS. 'TIS A NEW GRAVE I FILLED MYSELF.

MRS. MARCH IS FULL OF TRICKERY. NO DOUBT THE HEADSTONE FOR THAT STRANGE GIRL LUCY WENDOVER WAS FALSE TOO. ALL DONE TO SCARE ME — MAKE ME THINK SHE HAD COME FROM THE GRAVE.

WHERE ARE YOU OFF TO, MISS PRUDENCE?

ER — JUST GOING FOR A WALK. CLEAR MY HEAD. IT'S FAIR SPINNING WITH ALL THE EVENTS OF THE LAST FEW DAYS.

THERE'S LORD FARLEIGH'S MANSION. I ONLY HOPE HE'LL SEE ME AFTER COMING SO FAR.

But Lord Farleigh seemed kindness itself —

THANK YOU, YOUR LORDSHIP.

I'VE HEARD GOOD REPORTS OF YOUR FATHER AND WOULD LIKE TO HELP SUCH A FINE MAN. IF I CANNOT HELP YOU — MY LIBRARY HERE IS AT YOUR DISPOSAL. PERHAPS YOU'LL FIND SOMETHING THERE.

88

WHAT? WHO TOLD YOU THAT WAS MY NAME?

I WAS AN EVIL YOUTH, AYE, TRUE ENOUGH. BUT IT TORMENTED ME AND I CHANGED MY WAYS – AND MY NAME. IT SEEMED FIT I SHOULD IN FUTURE TEND THE DEAD.

AND THE WOMEN WHO DIED AS WITCHES?

SIR CLIVE KEPT THEIR SKULLS. WHEN HE DIED I TOOK THE COLLECTION AND STORED THEM IN THIS OLD ANGLO SAXON CRYPT. IT WAS THE LEAST I COULD DO FOR THE INNOCENT WRETCHES.

NO ONE – I MERELY WORKED IT OUT FROM A DESCRIPTION OF YOU IN A BOOK OF ENGLISH WITCHFINDERS.

THEY'D BE HERE NOW BUT FOR THAT CURSED STORM!

AYE – ONE. MARTHA RACKSTRAW. AND SHE VOWED SHE'D BE BACK – AND SHE IS.

WAS IT HER THAT PROMISED TO BURN LONDON?

AYE, IT WAS.

AND SHE'S IN THERE – PLANNING IT NOW!

IN – IN OUR HOUSE?

BUT WERE THERE REALLY ANY WITCHES AMONG THEM?

YOU MEAN THE WITCH MARTHA RACKSTRAW WHOM YOU AND SIR CLIVE BURNED ALL THOSE YEARS AGO HAS SOMEHOW TAKEN OVER OUR HOUSEKEEPER, MRS. MARCH?

AYE, MISS PRUDENCE, THAT'S THE SAD TRUTH. AND SHE'S PLANNING HER VENGEANCE ON THE WHOLE OF LONDON NOW.

Suddenly –

Nooooooo!

WHAT'S THAT TERRIBLE NOISE COMING FROM THE RECTORY?

A ragged woman ran out, and almost fell into Quist the gravedigger's arms.

THAT WOMAN IN THERE – SHE'S A FIEND! SHE'S KILLED MY GIRL.

CALM YOURSELF, WOMAN. TELL US WHAT HAPPENED.

SHE CAME TO ME – GAVE ME MONEY FOR MY LITTLE ALICE, SAID PARSON SYLVESTER WANTED A SERVANT. WE WERE STARVING. IT WAS LIKE A MIRACLE. BUT NOW SHE'S GONE –

THAT MUST BE LUCY SHE'S TALKING ABOUT. I DAREN'T TELL HER THAT HER DAUGHTER'S UNDER SOME STRANGE SPELL.

NOW SHE'S KILLED MY CHILD. I SAW HER IN THERE CARESSING POOR ALICE'S SKULL.

THAT WASN'T YOUR GIRL'S SKULL. YOUR DAUGHTER IS SAFE . . . SHE'S STAYING AT LORD FARLEIGH'S MANSION –

At that moment at Lord Farleigh's

THAT'S IT, MY BEAUTIES – BURN! BURN!

But later, in another street —

ANOTHER SKULL — AND IT JUST BURST INTO FLAMES!

SO THAT'S WHY THE FIRE IS SPREADING SO QUICKLY — THERE MUST BE SKULLS PLACED ALL OVER LONDON!

At last Prue made her way to the river.

THANK GOODNESS — THERE IS ROOM ON THAT BOAT! WE SHALL SOON BE BACK AT SAINT LEOFRIC'S — AND SAFETY.

But Lucy was waiting at the church gates —

LOOK AT LONDON BURN! ISN'T IT A BEAUTIFUL SIGHT?

POOR GIRL — SHE IS POSSESSED LIKE FATHER AND MRS. MARCH. SOMEHOW THE DEAD WITCH MARTHA RACKSTRAW MANAGES TO CONTROL THEM...

Then Quist, the gravedigger, appeared —

THE EVIL IS NOT YET DONE, MISS PRUE. EVEN NOW THAT WITCH MARTHA RACKSTRAW THROUGH MRS. MARCH IS PLANNING MORE VENGEANCE.

BURN YOUR HEART OUT, LONDON, AS ONCE YOU AND YOUR PEOPLE MERCILESSLY BURNED OURS.

AND NOW THIS CHURCH WHICH SHELTERED THOSE THAT HUNTED US AND GAVE US NO MERCY — IT SHALL BURN TO THE GROUND, TOO.

BUT WE CAN'T LET HER BURN FATHER'S CHURCH!

THERE'S NAUGHT WE CAN DO. LOOK INSIDE — SEE FOR YOURSELF.

WHEN THE SKULLS WERE FIRST DISCOVERED IN THE CRYPT, MRS. MARCH TOOK ONE TO HER ROOM. PERHAPS THAT WAS IT. I LOOKED FOR IT AFTERWARDS, BUT IT HAD GONE.

HMM. PERHAPS SHE PUT IT BACK IN THE CRYPT...IT'S CLUTCHING AT STRAWS, BUT WE MUST TRY.

NO USE. THE CRYPT'S EMPTY.

WAIT! LOOK THERE!

94